macy gray

Wise Publications
London | New York | Paris | Sydney | Copenhagen | Madrid | Tokyo

relating to a psychopath

Words by Macy Gray, Music by Jeremy Ruzumna, Darryl Swann & Dave Wilder

1. Hot like hot wings with hot choc-olate in hell. A - ha. Cold like in my i - so-
(Verse 2 see block lyric)

-la - tion cell— in the win — ter while I'm kiss — ing Mis — ter Freeze.

Take the wea - ther man and
(Verse 4 see block lyric)

throw him a - way. Hey, hey! Love is a de - sert and I need it to rain.— You

are so good at keep-ing me com-pa — ny.——

Play 4 times ad lib.

- by keep me com - pa - ny._____)

Love is but - ter, won't you be my bread?—

Did you hear what I said?_____

Drums

Verse 2:
Noah's elephants are leaving the ark in eights
During the upside of my manic depressive state
Crickets sing in 3 part harmony
I try to walk away I choke and I stumble
I'm flying back so listen close when I mumble
That you are so good at keeping me company.

You are relating to a psychopath *etc.*

Verse 4:
Cartoon figures dance in my head
I said
Love is butter won't you be my bread?
You are so good at keeping me company.

You are relating to a psychopath *etc.*

boo

Words by Macy Gray, Music by Jeremy Ruzumna, Darryl Swann,
Dave Wilder, Victor Indrizzo & Zac Rae

show, he's got dra - ma ev - 'ry day. Lots of

(Verse 3 see block lyric)

rage and men - tal a - bus - ing. The way he treats

me, it's ob - vi - ous he's con - fus - ing me for some

dumb bitch who will stick a - round. I tend to

stick a - - - round.

You tell me that you love me, if it's____ true, why am I run-ning from you, and

who, are these bitch-es on my an-swer ma - chine? Yeah,

you, tell me that you love me but____ boo, if this is love it's a

13

good thing you don't hate me.

Nev-er set-tle for— the things— that you don't real-ly want—'cause all it gets— you is— a big— ol' piece— of un-hap-pi-ness.— Could be mine and it's— so hard to talk— to you

Verse 2:
Superfly, someone who'll at least try
Who'll smoke me out from time to time
And love me all night
Tell me everything about him
And none of it turns out to be lies
Easy, rainbows, these words come to mind
And he loves me all night.

You, tell me that you love me if it's true *etc*.

Verse 3:
Hold me close 'cause I'm the most and
Make a toast to you and me
See that's the way, love's supposed to be
Not stressful… alright.

You, tell me that you love me if it's true *etc*.

sexual revolution

Words by Macy Gray, Music by Jeremy Ruzumna, Dave Wilder & Darryl Swann

Your ma-ma told you to be dis - creet_ and keep your freak to your - self._ But your ma - ma lied_ to you all this time. She knows as well as you and I___ you've got to ex - press what is ta - boo in you and share your freak with the rest of us. 'Cause it's a beau - ti - ful thing.

1.

I'm so fun-kin' beau - ti-ful, e - spe-cial-ly when I take my clothes off.

Verse 2:
Everybody break it
Every rule, every constriction
My papa told me to be home by now
But my party has just begun
Maybe he'll understand
That I got to be
To be the freak that God made me
So many things that I want to try
Got to do them before I die.

This is my sexual revolution *etc.*

hey young world part 2

Words & Music by Ricky Walters

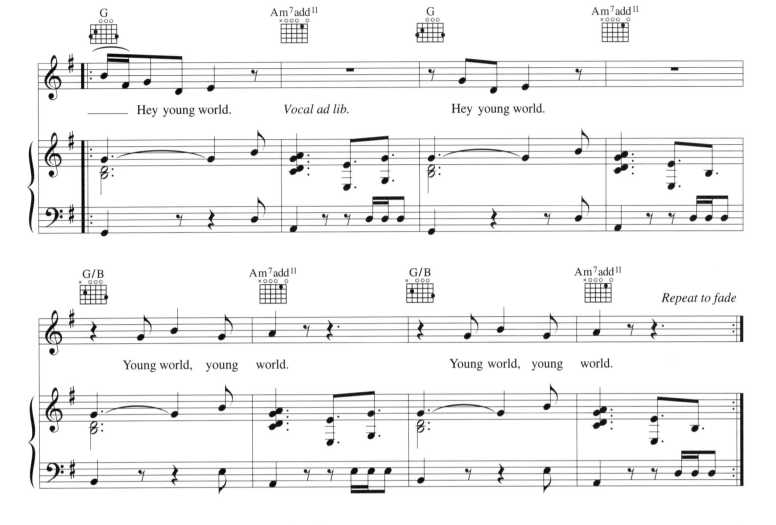

Verse 2:
Reward is a brainwashed kid gone wild
Young little girls already have a child
Bad company and now you've been framed
Parents are hurting so hurted and ashamed
Why?
Hey little kids don't follow these dopes
Why?
Don't be a fool like those who ditch school
It's yours.

Hey young world *etc.*

Verse 3:
Listen be strong
And scream
Woopie doo!
Go for yours
'Cause dreams come true
You'll make your mommy so proud of you too
And this is a message that the ruler rick threw
Why?

(Slick rick) *rap:*
Elders see our wise ones grow
Interest in what their kid learned 'bout
Seen how the offspring turned out
Knowing you can now safeguard self
Put upon an exciting path
You see immense pride they'll have.

sweet baby

Words by Macy Gray, Music by Joe Solo

Repeat ad lib. to fade

A - ha, sweet ba - by, life is cra - zy but there's_ one thing_ I'm sure_ of, that I'm your la - dy al - ways ba - by. *(Vocal ad lib.)*

32

harry

Words & Music by Macy Gray

1. Spe - cial lov - in' on the night I spent with you.— It was the
(Verse 2 see block lyric)

best that I've had late-ly. But it did-n't mean— a - ny - thing,

yeah,— and I will be glad when you stop call-in' me.—

Verse 2:
Swore my everlasting true love to you
Said that I need ya, I want ya didn't I
Baby
But I was just kiddin' 'round
And I will be glad when you stop callin' my house.

Harry *etc.*

don't come around

Words by Macy Gray, Music by Jeremy Ruzumna

make it   out of this war   a - live.   He brings me close and

says to me   "Let's make this a hap-py end - ing   and
(Verse 2 see block lyric)

try_____   to stay_____ friends."   But, you see,

if this love af - fair_____ was hap - py_____ then   it would not

end._____ And I___ don't wan - na be one of your friends,__

if we must break up then that's where it ends.___ So

please don't come a - round bring - ing me down.___

Lis - tening for your love I don't hear the sound.___ Oh, please___

Verse 2:
Don't invite me out to dinner
Don't call me on the phone
You wanted to leave me baby
So won't you leave me alone.

And I don't wanna be *etc.*

my nutmeg phantasy

Words by Macy Gray & Lonnie Marshall, Music by Lonnie Marshall, Keith Ciancia,
Tom Ralls, Finn Hammer & Darryl Swann

Verse 2:
Picture, if I was understanding
And you were less demanding
And the only time we scream and shout
Is when we're making love babe
On top of cloud 8
Believe in love and it will come down.

Nutty nutmeg phantasy *etc.*

gimme all your lovin'
or I will kill you

Words by Macy Gray, Music by Rita Marley, Arik Marshall, Jeremy Ruzumna & Darryl Swann

his moun-tains,— I've been swim-ming— all his seas.

No mat-ter what or how I tried,— I could-n't get the man to fall in love with me.

— Turns out he likes the girls with long and wa-vy hair.—

Mine is short and kin-ky. And I— have lost— my mind

49

Verse 2:
His whole body was shaking
And he holla'd when he fell to his knees
I held tighter to my a.k.a.
He said, "Please, please whatever you need"
See I have searched the wide world
To find the peace for the war in me
Don't wanna look no further
But you refuse to give it to me
And I have lost my mind.

C'mon and *etc.*

freak like me

Words by Macy Gray, Music by Eric Hord, Gary Zekley & Darryl Swann

the club."— Then we made love till my bo-dy ached.—

And ba-by when you have the time.— I wan-na tell you what is on my mind.—

I got-ta get it off 'cause it's so hea-vy.

Af-ter what we did the oth-er night— I wan-na be with you for all my life.—

Hey.

Ba - by when you have the time,— I wan - na tell you what is on my mind.—

I got - ta get it off 'cause it's so hea - vy.

Af - ter what we did the oth - er night— I wan - na be with you for all my life.—

forgiveness

Words by Macy Gray, Music by Darryl Swann & Hoyt Axton

Verse 2:
Please save a little for me
Where is the forgivness that you promised me
Am I too late?
Gone astray
Misplaced the keys to all my churches
Seems I've chased all of my angels away.

So I bleed
Gimme speed
While I'm running back to you
And I'll be nothing but true, true
Me you choose
See I was hopin' I could walk on your water with you.

Verse 3:
Forgiveness
Please send some down for me
Where is the forgiveness that you promised me?
Am I too late?
And I've learned to be still
When the beast within me moves
And I'll be nothing but true.

oblivion

Words by Macy Gray, Music Conceptualized by Brian Lester

Forget.

Bounce from right to left.

Here with the bro - ken heart - ed, let's get this par - ty start - ed

(Vocal ad lib.)

2°:
La la la la la la
I eat my marimbas
Oblivion
I tingle when I sing
Bling bling bling ting ting ting
Oblivion.

Forget
Bounce from right to left
Here with the broken hearted
Let's get this party started!

3°:
It's tempting to pack up your throne
Move in
Make this magic place your home
But nobody else can go
You'll be forever all alone.

Forget
Bounce from right to left
No longer broken hearted
And I don't know when it started.

shed

Words by Macy Gray, Music by Macy Gray, Darryl Swann & Jeremy Ruzumna

Am I___ still beau - ti - ful,_____ to you shed?

1. Did you know that I'm___ from a___ pla - net col - oured___ red.___
(Verse 2 see block lyric, 3° Instrumental)

Some - times___ at night___ car - toon___ fig - ures dance in my___ head.

For___ break-fast I like green eggs___ and___ stew

⊕ **Coda**

to you shed. Wel - come, this is— my life,—— and this here feel like lead.—

All my— de - fen - ces down,— all my lies are shed. Lies are shed.— *(Vocal ad lib.)*

Repeat ad lib. to fade

Verse 2:
I have favourites
Orange, heather, oats
And when it snows I, like to
Go outside and roll roll about
On Saturdays I lick lollipops and watch my pool
And deep inside I'm deep in love with you.

Exclusive distributors:
Music Sales Limited, 8/9 Frith Street, London W1B 3JB, England.
Music Sales Pty Limited, 120 Rothschild Avenue, Rosebery, NSW 2018, Australia.

Order No. AM972807
ISBN 0-7119-9208-8
This book © Copyright 2001 by Wise Publications.

Music arrangements by Derek Jones.
Music processed by Paul Ewers Music Design.

Printed in the United Kingdom by Caligraving Limited, Thetford, Norfolk.

Your Guarantee of Quality:
As publishers, we strive to produce every book to the highest commercial standards.
While endeavouring to retain the original running order of the recorded album,
the book has been carefully designed to minimise awkward
page turns and to make playing from it a real pleasure.
Particular care has been given to specifying acid-free, neutral-sized paper made from
pulps which have not been elemental chlorine bleached.
This pulp is from farmed sustainable forests and was produced with special regard for the environment.
Throughout, the printing and binding have been planned to ensure a sturdy,
attractive publication which should give years of enjoyment.
If your copy fails to meet our high standards, please inform us and we will gladly replace it.

Music Sales' complete catalogue describes thousands of titles and is available in
full colour sections by subject, direct from Music Sales Limited.
Please state your areas of interest and send a cheque/postal order for £1.50 for postage to:
Music Sales Limited, Newmarket Road, Bury St. Edmunds, Suffolk IP33 3YB.

www.musicsales.com